The School Hits of

Back to School 80s Hits

Wise Publications
part of The Music Sales Group
London / New York / Paris / Sydney / Copenhagen / Berlin / Madrid / Tokyo

Published by
Wise Publications
14-15 Berners Street, London, W1T 3LJ, UK.

Exclusive distributors:
Music Sales Limited
Distribution Centre, Newmarket Road,
Bury St Edmunds, Suffolk, IP33 3YB, UK.

Music Sales Pty Limited
120 Rothschild Avenue, Rosebery,
NSW 2018, Australia.

Order No. AM988273
ISBN 13: 978-1-84609-826-0
This book © Copyright 2007 Wise Publications,
a division of Music Sales Limited.

Compiled by Nick Crispin.
Edited by Fiona Bolton.
New arrangments by Joel Payne.
Music processed by Paul Ewers Music Design.

Cover design by the Design Corporation.

Printed in the EU.

Your Guarantee of Quality:
As publishers, we strive to produce every book
to the highest commercial standards.

Particular care has been given to specifying
acid-free, neutral-sized paper made from pulps
which have not been elemental chlorine bleached.

This pulp is from farmed sustainable forests
and was produced with special regard for the environment.

Throughout, the printing and binding have
been planned to ensure a sturdy, attractive
publication which should give years of enjoyment.

If your copy fails to meet our high standards,
please inform us and we will gladly replace it.

www.musicsales.com

Celebration

Words & Music by Ronald Bell, James Taylor, Robert Bell, George Brown,
Robert Mickens, Earl Toon, Claydes Smith, Dennis Thomas & Eumir Deodato

7

And The Beat Goes On

Words & Music by Leon Sylvers III, Stephen Shockley & William Shelby

And the beat goes on, just like my love, ev - er -

Dr. Beat

Words & Music by Enrique Garcia

Especially For You

Words & Music by Mike Stock, Matt Aitken & Pete Waterman

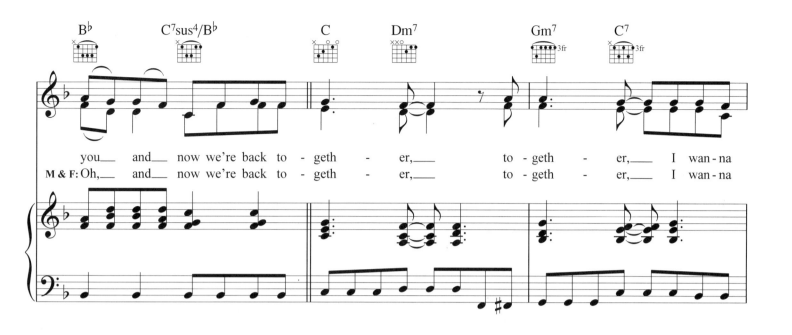

you__ and__ now we're back to - geth - er,__ to - geth - er,__ I wan - na

M & F: Oh,__ and__ now we're back to - geth - er,__ to - geth - er,__ I wan - na

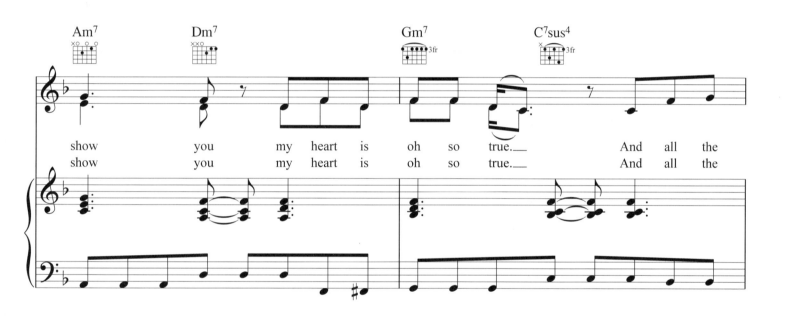

show you my heart is oh so true.__ And all the

show you my heart is oh so true.__ And all the

love I__ have is es - pe - cial - ly__ for__ you.__

love I__ have is es - pe - cial - ly__ for__ you.__

21

F: 3. Es - pe - cial - ly___ for you,___

F: You were in___ my___

heart, my love nev - er changed.___

23

Girls Just Want To Have Fun

Words & Music by Robert Hazard

I come up in the morn-ing light,— my moth-
Phone rings in the mid-dle of the night,— my bud-

-er says when— you gon-na live your life right?
-dy asks— what you gon-na do with your life?

Oh ma-ma dear— we're not the for-tu-nate ones, and
Oh dad-dy dear— you know you're still num-ber one, but

girls— they want to have fun, woah— girls— they want to have...

25

D.S. al Coda

𝄋 *Coda*

26

rest of the world, I wan-na be the one to walk in the sun.

Hey now, hey now, what's the mat-ter with you, girls just want to have fun now. Hey now, hey now, what's the mat-ter with you,

Gloria

Words & Music by Giancarlo Bigazzi & Umberto Tozzi

1. Glo - ri - a, you're al - ways on the run, now,___

3. Glo - ri - a, how's_ it gon - na go down?___

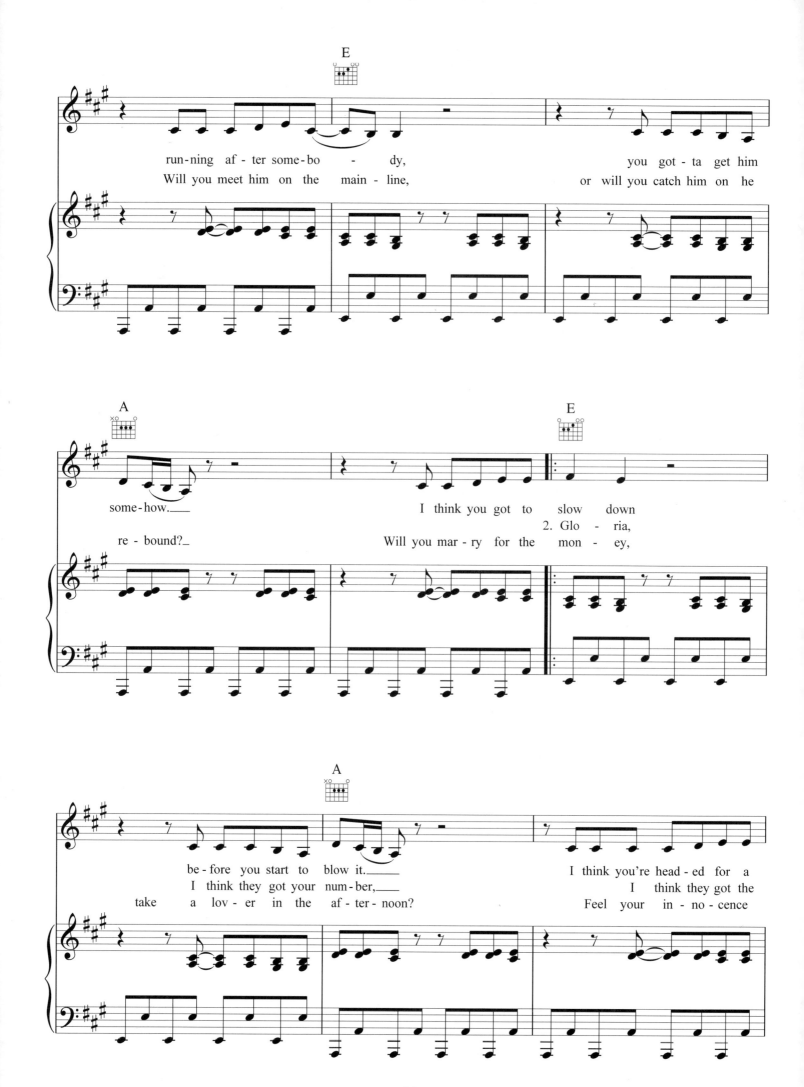

call-ing, 'Glo - ri - a'?

call-ing, 'Glo - ri - a'?

call-ing, 'Glo - ri - a'?

1, 3.

Glo - ri - a,   don't_ you think you're fal - ling?

If ev-'ry-bo - dy wants   you,   why is-n't an - y - bo - dy

I Think We're Alone Now

Words & Music by Ritchie Cordell

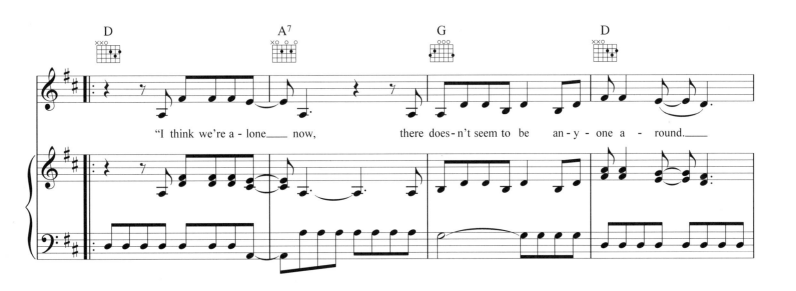

"I think we're a-lone____ now, there does-n't seem to be an-y-one a-round.____

I think we're a-lone____ now, the beat-ing of our hearts is the on-ly sound."____

Repeat and fade

41

Just Can't Get Enough

Words & Music by Vince Clarke

When I'm with you, ba - by, I go out__ of my head. And I just can't get e-nough, and I
We walk to-geth-er we're walk-ing__ down the street. And I just can't get e-nough, and I
And when it rains__ you're shin-ing down__ for__ me. And I just can't get e-nough,

*Tacet 3rd time till *

43

just can't get e - nough,_ I just can't get e - nough,_ I just can't get e - nough,_ I

just can't get e - nough,_ I just can't get e - nough,_ I just can't get e - nough,_ I

Mickey

Words & Music by Nicky Chinn & Mike Chapman

1. Hey, Mick ey! You've

3. Hey, Mick ey! Now when you

(1.) been a-round all night and that's a lit - tle long. You think you've got the right but I
(2.) when you say you will, it al-ways means you won't. You're giv - ing me the chills, ba - by,
(3.) take me by the who's ev - er gon - na know? Ev - 'ry time you move I let a
(4.) come on and give it to me an - y way you can. An - y way you wan-na do it, I'll

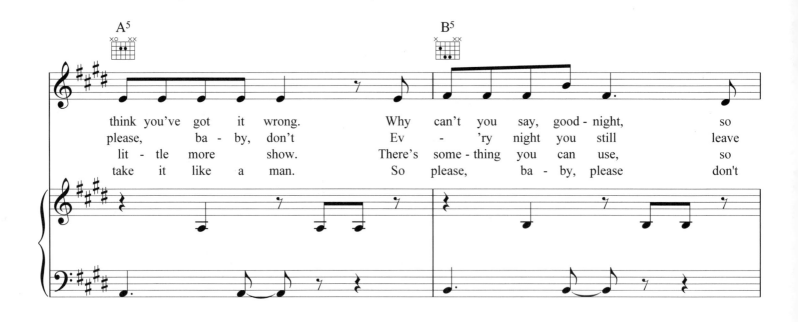

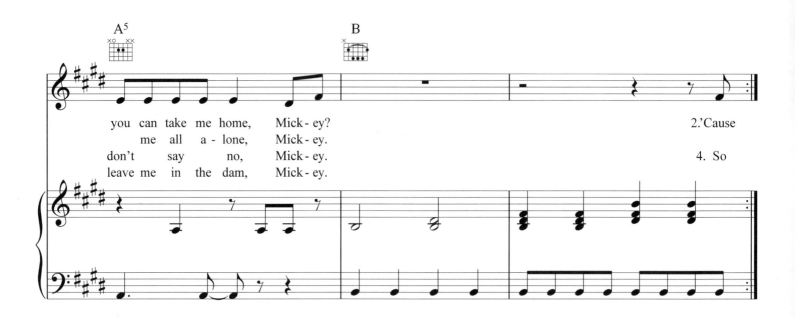

49

50

The Only Way Is Up

Words & Music by George Jackson & Johnny Henderson

Repeat and fade

55

Tainted Love

Words & Music by Ed Cobb

Take On Me

Words & Music by Morten Harket,
Mags Furuholmen & Pal Waaktaar

Ba ba ba ba__ ba.

1. Talk - ing__ a - way,
(Verses 2 & 3 see block lyric)
I don't know__ what I'm to say. I'll

say it an - y - way.__ To - day is an - no - ther day_____ to find you.

Verse 2
So, needless to say,
I'm odds and ends but I'm me
Stumbling away.
Slowly learning that life is O.K.
Say after me:
It's no better to be safe than sorry.

Take on me *etc.*

Verse 3
Oh, the things that you say,
Is it life or just a play?
My worries away,
You're all the things I've got to remember.
You're shying away,
I'll be coming for you anyway.

Take on me *etc.*

Waiting For A Star To Fall

Words & Music by George Merrill & Shannon Rubicam

-ting makes me love____ you____ e - ven more.____

Instrumental

Wait

Upside Down

Words & Music by Bernard Edwards & Nile Rodgers

cher - ish__ the mo - ments__ with you.
cra - zy__ to think you__ are mine.

Re - spect-ful-ly,__ I say__ to thee, I'm a -
As long__ as__ the__ sun_____ con-

- ware that__ you're cheat-ing, when no - one makes me feel like you do.
- ti - nues__ to shine,__ there's a place__ in my heart for you, that's the bot-tom line.

1, 2.

3.

F#m7   B7   E   F#m7

Up - side down, boy, you turn__ me.__

B7   E   F#m7

In - side out and round,__ round.__

Repeat and fade

75

You Spin Me Round (Like A Record)

Words & Music by Peter Burns, Stephen Coy, Tim Lever & Michael David